MAKE AND COLOUR

SPOOKY THINGS

Clare Beaton

b small publishing

How to use this book

Pull out the centre black and white pages of the book. These are ready-drawn cards, masks and decorations for you to colour. **Cut along the solid lines and fold along the dotted lines.**

For colouring in, you can use coloured pencils, crayons, felt-tip pens or paints. Start colouring the centre of the cut-outs first. Leave borders for last so you don't smudge them.

Use fairly thick paint and wash your brush between colours. Leave the cut-outs flat to dry. Don't forget to add your signature on the back of the cards!

On the inside back cover there is a template which can be used to make envelopes for some of the cards. Then you can post them to your family and friends.

Keep the rest of the book. It has lots of other ideas on how to make more spooky things. There are also templates and stencils to help you.

Some things you will need:
★ plain and coloured paper or thin card
★ tracing paper
★ pencil and ruler
★ scissors and craft knife
★ glue
★ sticky tape
★ black bin liners
★ gold and silver paints
★ crayons, paints and felt-tip pens
★ thread and thin elastic

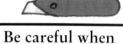

Be careful when using a craft knife.

2

Templates

When you are tracing from the templates on page 5 or the inside covers, here is how to do it very simply and successfully.

What you will need:

★ tracing paper
★ soft pencil
★ sticky tape
★ paper or card

1

Trace the template shape with the pencil. Tape down the tracing paper to keep it still.

2

Turn over the tracing paper and scribble over the lines with the soft pencil.

3

Turn over again and tape on to the card or paper. Retrace firmly over the lines. Remove the tracing paper.

Stencils

Cut along the perforated line and remove the sheet of stencils from the back cover of the book. You will need them for some of the creepy things in this book.

What you will need:

★ coloured paper or card
★ pencil
★ scissors

1

Place the stencil shape on the card or paper. Draw inside the shape with a pencil.

2

Colour in the outline shape or cut it out with scissors and use to decorate your spooky things.

3

Witch's Hat

Make a witch's hat from stiff black paper.

Cut a triangle from black paper. Roll it into a cone and tape along the edge. Cut along the edge to make it straight.

41 cm

70 cm

7 cm

1 Stand it on more black paper. Draw a circle around the cone.

2 Then draw another circle 7 cm larger than the first.

3 Cut out a circle 3 cm inside the smaller circle. Cut a fringe around edge up to centre circle.

4 Cut out large circle.

5 Fold the fringe up and tape it inside the cone.

Use the stencil to draw shapes on to coloured paper. Cut out and stick on the hat.

Before you begin you could use the stencil and gold or silver paint to decorate the black paper.

Mini mask – for your favourite toy animal.

Masks

Colour the masks. Cut them out.
Take care when you cut the eye
holes. Thread thin elastic on to a
large needle. Thread through the
holes. Knot the ends.

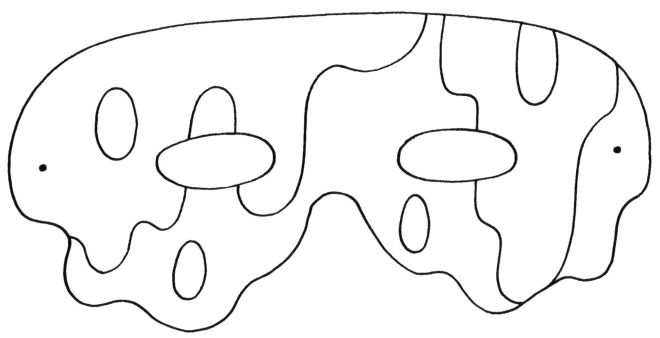

Before you thread the elastic, strengthen
the holes by sticking tape on the back.

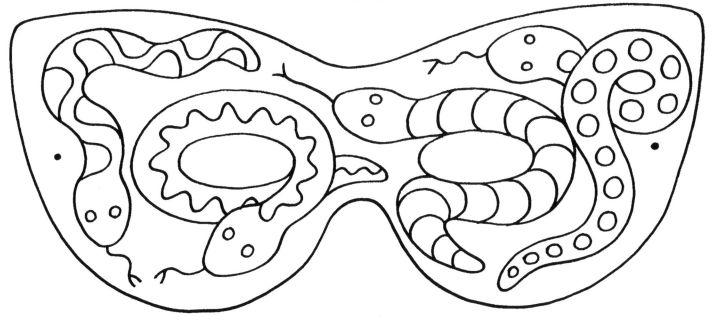

FOLD

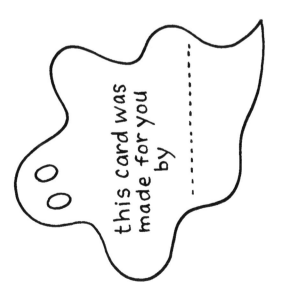

this card was
made for you
by
_ _ _ _ _ _ _

Goblins,
Ghosties and
Ghouls
to you!

Party name cards

Colour in. Write the name on the bottom half of the cards. Use a craft knife to cut out the shape *above* the dotted lines. Fold along the dotted lines.

Spooky decorations
Colour in bright orange,
purple, red and lime green.
Cut out and hang up with
lengths of black thread.

Spooky fortune teller

Colour in. Make each star a different colour. Write a spooky message in each of the empty triangles. Cut out the teller and fold as follows:

Put a forefinger and thumb of each hand into the four pockets and close the teller.

Ask a friend to say a small number. Open and close the teller that number of times. Open and ask them to choose a colour. Open and read the message underneath.

this card was
made for you
by

· · · · · · · · · · · ·

this card was
made for you by

· · · · · · · · · · · · · · · · · ·

CUT

**Sludge and Slime
Have a good time!**

**Have a
purrrfect day!**

Skull face mask

Colour in black around the eye holes, nostrils and jaw. Cut out the mask. Take care with the eye holes.

Then thread elastic through the holes. Strengthen the holes with sticky tape on the back.

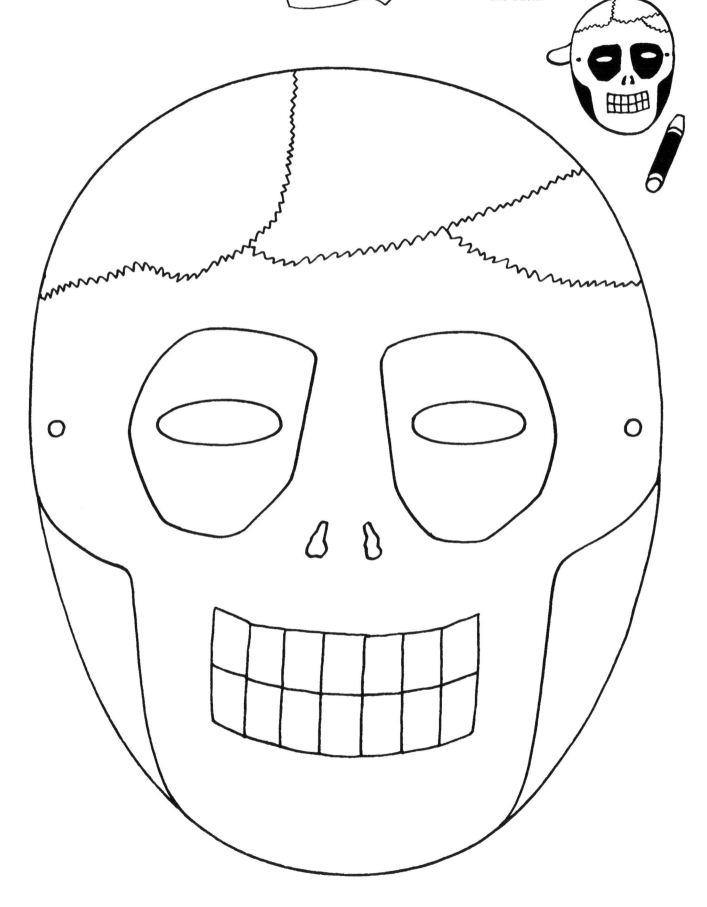

Paint or draw the stencil shapes on to stiff paper. Cut them out. Then tape short lengths of black thread on to the shapes. Tape them under the brim of the hat.

Horns

Following the instructions on page 3 for templates, draw two horns on to thin card or stiff paper. Use white or dayglo paper or paint with dripping blood!

Cut out the horns including the slit at the bottom. Wind the two pieces, as shown, around either side of a hair band. Secure with sticky tape.

Invitations

Use the template on the inside of the front cover. Then follow the instructions on page 3 to trace the skull and crossbones on paper.

Paint or draw around them to the edge of the paper, or leave a rough, uneven edge.

Spider's web

Cut a six-sided shape from coloured paper. Using a black pen draw on the web lines. Stencil a black spider in the centre.

Spooky writing

Try writing one word – PARTY or a friend's name - in special spooky letters.

Paint some slime around your card.

wobbly   slimy   spider webs

Don't forget to write the party details on the back of your card.
where
when
fancy dress
RSVP telephone number

Spooky doorway

Decorate a doorway with black plastic bin liners cut into strips. For really long streamers, cut the sides of the bags and double the length of the strips.

Don't cut right to the top.

Draw the stencil shapes on to stiff paper and cut them out. Tape the end of some black thread to the centre of the shapes. Hang them on the streamers.

Tape along the top of a door – and make a surprise entry!

Envelopes

Make some colourful envelopes for your cards using the template on the inside back cover.

What you will need:
★ coloured paper
★ pencil
★ tracing paper
★ ruler
★ scissors
★ glue

1

Follow the instructions on page 3 to trace the template on to paper, using a ruler to help. Cut it out.

2

Fold along the dotted lines. Glue the bottom flap on to the two side flaps. Put the card in and glue down the top flap.

Use the stencils to decorate the envelopes.

Emma

Joe Brown
17 High Road
Moorton
Yorkshire
B21 X73